The Pianist's Collection

Book Three
Selected & Edited by Alan Ridout

Kevin Mayhew

We hope you enjoy *The Pianist's Collection Book 3*.
Further copies of this and the other books in the series are available
from your local music shop.

In case of difficulty, please contact the publisher direct:

The Sales Department
KEVIN MAYHEW LTD
Rattlesden
Bury St Edmunds
Suffolk IP30 0SZ

Phone 0449 737978
Fax 0449 737834

Front Cover: *Lunch at Villeneuve-sur-Yonne* by Edouard Vuillard (1868-1940).
Reproduced by courtesy of the Trustees, The National Gallery, London.
Cover designed by Juliette Clarke and Graham Johnstone.

First published in Great Britain in 1992 by Kevin Mayhew Ltd.

© Copyright 1992 Kevin Mayhew Ltd.

ISBN 0 86209 252 3

All or part of these pieces have been edited by
Alan Ridout and are the copyright of Kevin Mayhew Ltd.

Series Music Editor: Anthea Smith.

Printed and bound in Great Britain.

Contents

ALAN RIDOUT (b. 1934), who selected and edited the music in this book, is one of England's most prolific composers, producing a steady stream of works in most forms: symphonies, operas, ballet music, chamber music, song cycles and church music.

He studied with Gordon Jacob and Herbert Howells at the Royal College of Music and later with Peter Racine Fricker, Michael Tippett, and the Dutch composer Henk Badings. He has taught at four universities, including Oxford and Cambridge, and for over twenty years was also a Professor at the Royal College of Music.

CRADLE SONG

Edvard Grieg (1843-1907)

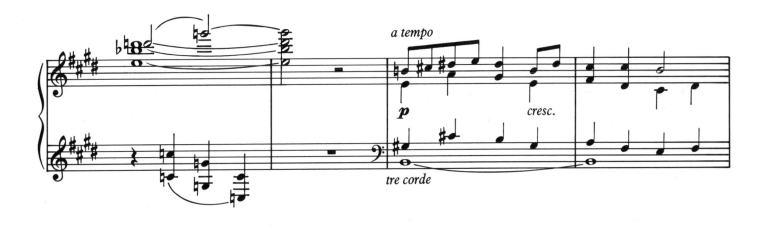

COUNTRY DANCE

James Hook (1746-1827)

FOUNTAIN SPRINGS

Enrique Granados (1867-1916)

Allegretto tranquillo ($\quarternote = 100$)

MINUET IN D

Ludwig van Beethoven (1770-1827)

PU octaves

D.C. al Fine

13

ON THE LAKE

Heinrich Hofmann (1842-1902)

MAZURKA

Peter Ilyich Tchaikovsky (1840-1893)

FINALE from Sonata No. 24

Joseph Haydn (1732-1809)

21

PRELUDE IN G

Alexander Scriabin (1872-1915)

SONATINA

Thomas Attwood (1765-1838)

GYMNOPÉDIE III

Erik Satie (1866-1925)

PRELUDE IN B MINOR

Frédéric Chopin (1810-1849)

CANTABILE

Ludwig van Beethoven (1770-1827)

WALTZ IN A

Isaac Albéniz (1860-1909)

34

STARLIGHT

Edward MacDowell (1860-1908)

ALLEGRETTO

Felix Mendelssohn (1809-1847)

BOHEMIAN WALTZ

Samuel Coleridge-Taylor (1875-1912)

41

42

Tempo I

WALTZ IN A FLAT

Ludwig van Beethoven (1770-1827)

Fine

D.C. al Fine

45

SHEHERAZADE

Robert Schumann (1810-1856)